KS2
Success

Science

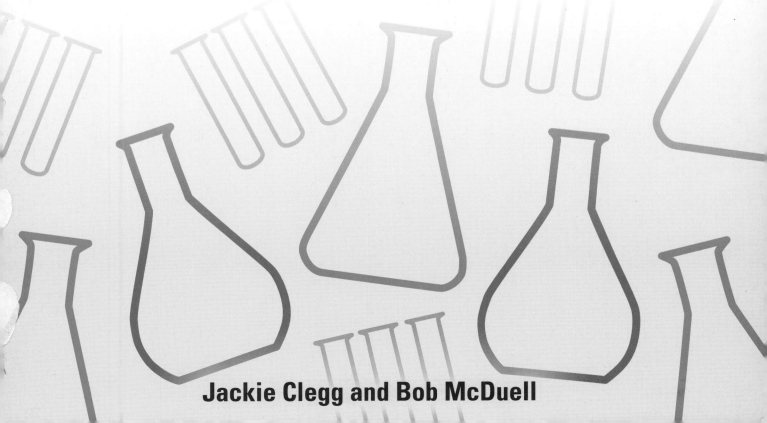

Jackie Clegg and Bob McDuell

Contents

Introduction

Sets
ABC

KEY STAGE 2
Levels 3–5
Introduction

Science

Introduction

Instructions on using the Practice Test Papers

Understanding Assessment

What is assessment?

Teacher assessment and national test results are used to determine your child's level of attainment at the end of Key Stage 2 (at the age of 11).

What are the children tested and assessed on?

The national tests are designed to test children's knowledge and understanding of specific elements of the Key Stage 2 curriculum in English and Maths.

Pupils at some schools also take part in Science sampling tests and the results are used to monitor national standards.

Your child's teacher will also assess their learning at other times. Teacher assessment covers English, Maths and Science.

How these Tests will Help your Child

1   These test papers will help you to assess your child's progress throughout Year 6. The papers provide a good idea of the strengths and weaknesses of your child's scientific knowledge.

2   The Answers and Mark Scheme have been provided to allow you to check how your child has done.

3   When an area of weakness has been identified, it is useful to go over these and similar types of questions with your child. Sometimes your child will be familiar with the subject matter but might not understand what the question is asking. This will become apparent when talking to your child.

Tips for the Top

1   **Don't make silly mistakes.** Make sure you emphasise to your child the importance of reading the question carefully. Easy marks can be picked up by just doing as the question asks. Common mistakes are things like ticking just one answer when the question asks for two ticks.

2   **Make your answers clearly legible.** If your child has made a mistake, encourage them to put a cross through it and write the correct answer clearly next to it. Try to encourage your child to use an eraser as little as possible.

3   **Don't panic!** Explain to your child that there is no need to worry if they cannot do a question, just go on to the next question and come back to the problem later if they have time.

Instructions for Parents

1   Make sure you provide your child with a quiet environment where they can complete their test undisturbed.

2   Provide your child with the following equipment: **pencil**, **ruler** and **eraser** (rubber).

3   Each of the six test papers is 45 minutes long.

Marking the Tests and Assessing Levels

1   Make sure your child has completed all the relevant tests, e.g. Set A Test Paper 1 and Set A Test Paper 2.

2   Mark the practice test papers using the answers provided in the pull-out Answers and Mark Scheme.

3   Add up the marks on each paper. Test Paper 1 is marked out of 40 and Test Paper 2 is marked out of 40. This gives a maximum total of 80 marks.

4   Write the marks in the corresponding table below.

	Set A
Test Paper 1 (out of 40)	
Test Paper 2 (out of 40)	
TOTAL (out of 80)	

	Set B
Test Paper 1 (out of 40)	
Test Paper 2 (out of 40)	
TOTAL (out of 80)	

	Set C
Test Paper 1 (out of 40)	
Test Paper 2 (out of 40)	
TOTAL (out of 80)	

Once you have your total mark out of 80 look at the table below to find out which National Curriculum level it matches to.

Level	Mark range (total/80)
Below Level 3	0–17
3	18–40
4	41–60
5	61–80

Please note: these tests are **only a guide** to the level your child can achieve and cannot guarantee the same level is achieved during their Key Stage 2 assessments.

It is expected that the majority of 11 year old children will achieve Level 4 by the end of Year 6. However, for some children, achieving Level 3 is a real success for that individual. A child achieving Level 5 is working to a high level and, in exceptional cases, a child may reach Level 6.

Test Paper 1

Instructions:

- find a quiet place where you can sit down and complete the test paper undisturbed

- make sure you have all the necessary equipment to complete the test paper

- read the questions carefully

- answer all the questions in this test paper

- go through and check your answers when you have finished the test paper

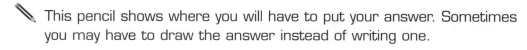 This pencil shows where you will have to put your answer. Sometimes you may have to draw the answer instead of writing one.

Time:

This test paper is **45 minutes** long.

Note to Parents:

Check how your child has done against the Answers and Mark Scheme on pages 97–104.

Page	7	9	11	13	15	17	19	Max. Mark	**Actual Mark**
Score	....	....	....	....	....	....	....	40	....

First name _____

Last name _____

Different Materials

1   Ali has some blocks made of different materials.

The blocks are all the same size.

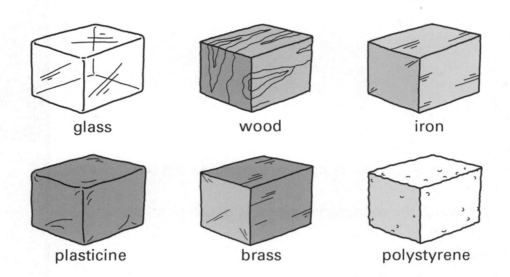

glass   wood   iron

plasticine   brass   polystyrene

a) The glass block is 'transparent'.

What is meant by the word 'transparent'?

_____

_____ *(1 mark)*

Q1a

b) Which block could be made into a magnet?

_____ *(1 mark)*

Q1b

c) One block can be easily reshaped.

Which block is this?

✎ _____ (1 mark)

d) Which two blocks would float in water?

✎ _____

and _____ (2 marks)

e) Arrange the three blocks in this list in order of increasing hardness.

iron   polystyrene   wood

✎ least hard _____

_____

hardest _____

(2 marks)

f) i Ali buys some polystyrene tiles and sticks them to the ceiling in the kitchen.

Suggest why Ali might have done this.

✎ _____

_____ (1 mark)

ii Write down **TWO** properties of polystyrene that make it suitable for this use.

✎ _____

_____ (2 marks)

(Total 10 marks)

On the Farm

2   Class 4C visit a farm.

The farmer shows the children the plants he grows.

a) **Why does the farmer grow lots of plants?**

✎ _____ *(1 mark)*

b) The children see rabbits eating the farmer's carrots.

The farmer says the fox eats some of the rabbits.

Draw the food chain by writing the words in the boxes.

Choose the words from this list.

carrots   **fox**   **rabbits**

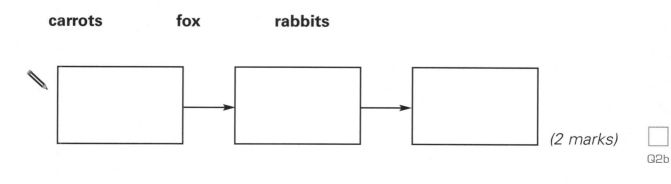

(2 marks)

c) Put a ring around the part of the food chain that is a predator.

    carrots   **fox**   **rabbits**   *(1 mark)*

d) The farmer will soon dig up his carrots.

What effect will this have on the rabbits?

_____

_____ *(1 mark)*

(Total 5 marks)

Drying the Washing

3 Kim hangs wet washing on a clothes line.

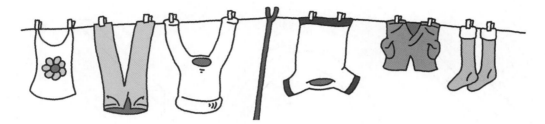

The washing dries without it raining.

a) Write down **TWO** things that will help the washing to dry quickly.

✎ _____

_____ *(2 marks)* ☐
Q3a

b) Finish the sentence by using the best word from this list.

boiling   evaporating   freezing   melting

✎ When the clothes dry, the water is _____ *(1 mark)* ☐
Q3b

c) In the evening the washing is dry. Kim forgets to bring in the washing.
Next morning the washing is wet, even though it did not rain in the night.
Suggest the most likely reason for this happening.

✎ _____

_____ *(2 marks)* ☐
Q3c

(Total 5 marks)

subtotal

Strong Magnet

4 Chris has three magnets.

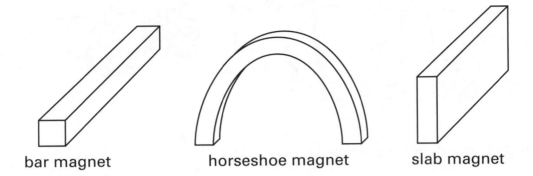

bar magnet   horseshoe magnet   slab magnet

He is trying to find out which is the strongest magnet.

Chris finds out that each magnet can pick up paper clips.

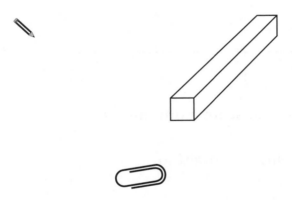

a) Draw an arrow to show the pull of the magnet on the paper clip. *(1 mark)*

Q4

b) Chris finds out how many paper clips each magnet can pick up.

Here are his results.

Magnet	Number of paper clips
bar	26
horseshoe	20
slab	35

Finish the bar chart. Draw a bar to show how many paper clips each magnet picked up.

One bar has been done for you.

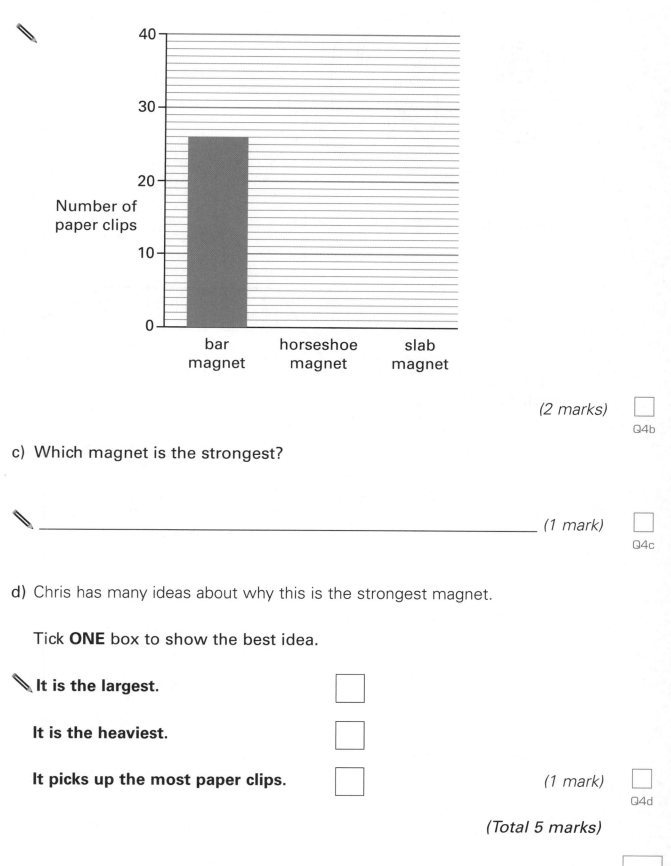

(2 marks)

c) Which magnet is the strongest?

_____ *(1 mark)*

d) Chris has many ideas about why this is the strongest magnet.

Tick **ONE** box to show the best idea.

It is the largest. ☐

It is the heaviest. ☐

It picks up the most paper clips. ☐ *(1 mark)*

(Total 5 marks)

Pulse Rate

5 Jenny wears a pulse rate meter attached to her ear lobe.

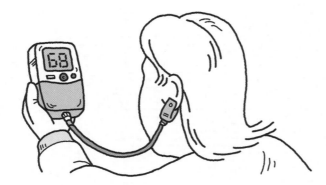

She records her pulse rate at playtime.

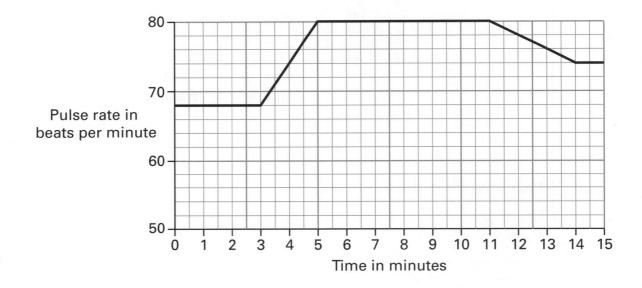

a) What was Jenny's highest pulse rate?

✎ _____ beats per minute   *(1 mark)*

b) What was Jenny's pulse rate at 3 minutes?

✎ _____ beats per minute   *(1 mark)*

c) After 3 minutes Jenny started to run around.

How can you tell this from the graph?

✎ _____

_____ (1 mark)

d) Why does Jenny's pulse rate change as she is running?

✎ _____

_____

_____ (2 marks)

e) For how many minutes is Jenny running around?

✎ _____ minutes   (1 mark)

(Total 6 marks)

Keeping the Coffee Warm

6 Abdul wants to find out which material will keep his coffee warm.

He makes his coffee from boiled water.

Abdul uses sensors connected to a computer to measure the temperature every 5 minutes.

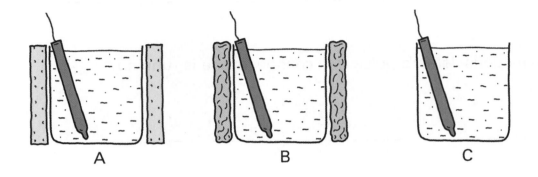

A   B   C

The graph shows his results.

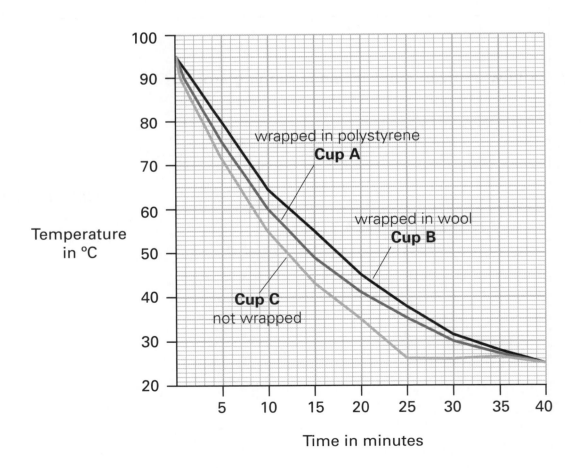

Temperature in °C

Time in minutes

a) What temperature was the coffee in **Cup A** at 25 minutes?

_____°C (1 mark)

b) Tick **ONE** box to show in which cup the coffee cooled the fastest.

Cup A ☐   **Cup B** ☐   **Cup C** ☐   (1 mark)

c) Use the graph. Estimate the temperature of the room.

_____°C (1 mark)

d) Complete the sentence. Choose words from this list.

electrical conductor   **thermal insulator**   **thermal conductor**

The material that keeps the coffee warm is a good

_____ (1 mark)

e) Describe one other way that Abdul could help to stop heat leaving his coffee to keep it warmer for longer.

_____

_____ (1 mark)

(Total 5 marks)

Mirrors and Light Rays

7 Jamil cycles home from school.

He approaches a sharp bend in the road.

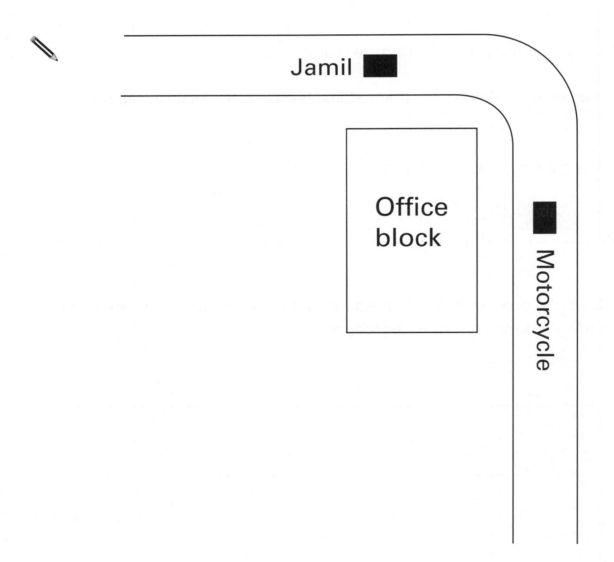

a) Show, by drawing light rays on the diagram on page 18, how a mirror placed at the bend in the road could enable Jamil to see the motorcycle.

(2 marks)

b) Why can he not see the motorcycle coming towards him around the bend?

✎ _____

_____ *(1 mark)*

c) Which word best describes what happens when a light ray hits the mirror? Choose the word from this list.

radiates   **rebounds**   **reflects**

✎ _____ *(1 mark)*

(Total 4 marks)

END OF TEST

Set
A

KEY STAGE 2
Levels 3–5

Test Paper 2

Science

Test Paper 2

Test Paper 2

Instructions:

- find a quiet place where you can sit down and complete the test paper undisturbed
- make sure you have all the necessary equipment to complete the test paper
- read the questions carefully
- answer all the questions in this test paper
- go through and check your answers when you have finished the test paper

This pencil shows where you will have to put your answer. Sometimes you may have to draw the answer instead of writing one.

Time:

This test paper is **45 minutes** long.

Note to Parents:

Check how your child has done against the Answers and Mark Scheme on pages 97–104.

Page	21	23	25	27	29	31	33	35	Max. Mark	**Actual Mark**
Score	....	....	....	....	....	....	....	....	40	....

First name ....

Last name ....

Circuits

1 Emily is setting up an electrical circuit. She has wires, switches, bulbs and cells (batteries). She does not use them all.

a) Draw three lines to match each drawing to its symbol.

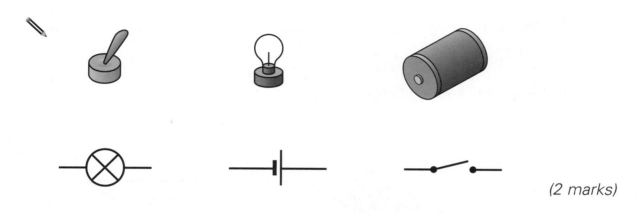

(2 marks)

Look at the picture of Emily's circuit.

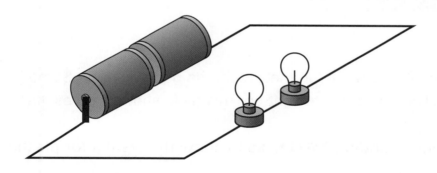

b) Use the symbols to draw a diagram of Emily's circuit. *(1 mark)*

The bulbs in Emily's circuit are very bright. Emily removes a cell (battery) from the circuit.

c) Complete the sentence below to describe the effect on the bulbs of removing a cell.

The bulbs will be _____ *(1 mark)*

d) Emily adds some different materials to her circuit.

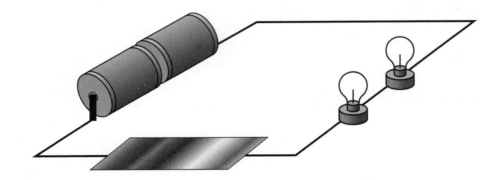

When some materials are placed in the circuit, the bulbs light up. Some materials do not allow the bulbs to light up. This table shows her results.

i Finish the table by adding **TWO ticks** to show the results for plastic and iron.

Material	Bulbs light up	Bulbs do not light up
tin	✓	
plastic		
iron		

(1 mark)

ii Finish these sentences. Choose your words from this list.

conductor   **elastic**   **insulator**

Copper allows electricity to pass through the circuit. Copper is a/an

_____

Wood does not allow electricity to pass through the circuit. Wood is a/an

_____   *(2 marks)*

(Total 7 marks)

Earth, Sun and Moon

2 Jane and Becky are talking to Class 6B about the Earth, the Sun and the Moon. They are using models (a football, a pea and a small bead) to represent the Earth, the Sun and the Moon.

a) Draw three lines to match each model to what it represents.

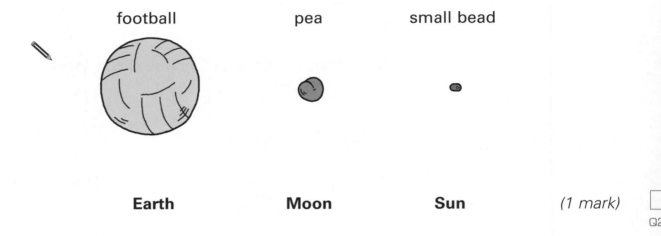

football   pea   small bead

Earth   **Moon**   **Sun**   *(1 mark)*

b) Jane will show how the Earth orbits the Sun. Becky is pretending to be the Sun and stands in the middle of the room.

Draw the path Jane should walk around Becky to show the Earth's orbit.

Becky

Jane

(1 mark)

c) Jane has some ideas about the Earth, the Sun and the Moon.

Write **true** or **false** below each idea.

1 It takes the Earth a year to make one complete orbit around the Sun.

_____

2 The Earth does not spin as it orbits the Sun.

_____

3 It takes the Moon about 28 days to orbit the Earth.

_____

(2 marks)

(Total 4 marks)

Experiments with Evaporating

3 Sue and Sam are carrying out an experiment to see how fast evaporation takes place. They are going to measure out some water and leave it in a shallow dish. Every day they are going to measure the volume of water that remains.

Here is a table of their results.

	Start	Day 1	Day 2	Day 3	Day 4	Day 5
Volume of water in cm^3	50	34	25	18	9	0

subtotal

a) Finish the bar chart to show their results at day 2, day 3, day 4 and day 5.

(2 marks)

b) After how many days has half the water evaporated?

_____ *(1 mark)*

c) Different liquids evaporate at different rates under the same conditions.
Put the three liquids in this list in order of how quickly they evaporate.
Put the liquid that evaporates fastest first.

motor oil   **petrol**   **water**

evaporates fastest   _____

_____

evaporates slowest   _____   *(2 marks)*

(Total 5 marks)

Plants

4 Tim grows lots of plants. Some of the plants are for Tim to eat.

a) Circle the **TWO** that Tim would be most likely to eat.

grass   apple   lettuce   daffodil   *(2 marks)*

Q4a

Some of the plants are grown in pots.

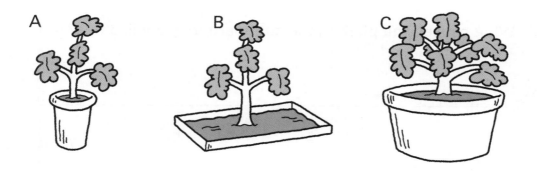

b) Explain why **Plant A** and **Plant B** are not growing as well as **Plant C**.

_____

_____ *(2 marks)*

Q4b

subtotal

c) Tim's mum put some plants in the garden. One plant was left in a dark cupboard.

Plants in garden   Plant left in cupboard

i   Describe **TWO** things that are different about the plant left in the cupboard.

✎ _____

_____ (2 marks)

Q4c

ii   What caused the plant in the cupboard to grow like this?

✎ _____ (1 mark)

Q4c

(Total 7 marks)

Soil

5 Alan is making a new garden at his house. He looks at the soil and finds that there are many small pebbles in the soil. He needs to remove the pebbles before he can sow grass for a lawn.

a) **What piece of equipment does he use to remove pebbles from the soil?**

✎ _____ *(1 mark)*

Q5a

b) He takes samples from two different places in the garden. He puts each sample of soil into a funnel and adds water.

He times how long it takes for the water to pass through the soil into the beaker.

Write down two things that he should do to ensure this is a fair test.

✎ _____ and

_____ *(2 marks)*

Q5b

c) He finds out that sandy soil has large particles but clay soil has much smaller particles.

Which type of soil – sandy or clay – will let the water pass through faster?

✎ _____

Explain your answer.

✎ _____

_____ *(1 mark)*

(Total 4 marks)

Using a Key

6   Class 6 visit a farm. They see these animals.

cow   fish   worm   duck

a) Tick **TWO** boxes that show the two animals that need water in their habitat.

cow ☐   **fish** ☐   **worm** ☐   **duck** ☐   *(1 mark)* ☐

Q6a

Class 6 sort the animals using a key.

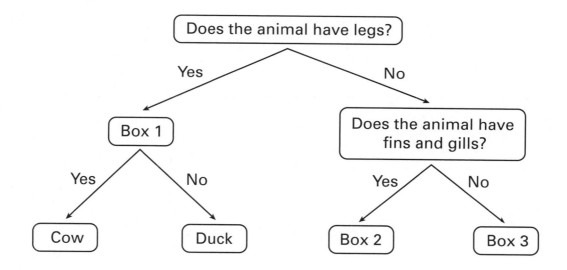

b) Tick **ONE** box to show what should be written in Box 1.

Does the animal have legs?   ☐

Does the animal have two legs?   ☐

Does the animal have more than two legs?   ☐   *(1 mark)* ☐

Q6b

c) What should be written in Box 2? Circle the correct word.

✎   **cow**   **duck**   **fish**   **worm**   *(1 mark)*

Q6c

d) What should be written in Box 3? Circle the correct word.

✎   **cow**   **duck**   **fish**   **worm**   *(1 mark)*

Q6d

e) Tick **ONE** box to show the reason why we classify animals.

✎ **To group animals that live in water**   ☐

   To help identify animals   ☐

   To help draw a food chain   ☐   *(1 mark)*

Q6e

(Total 5 marks)

Concert

7 Liam, Scott and Jason go to a rock concert. Liam stands near the stage. Scott and Jason are further back.

Jason   Scott   Liam

a) Who hears the loudest noise? Tick **ONE** box.

✎ **Jason** ☐   **Liam** ☐   **Scott** ☐   *(1 mark)* ☐

Q7a

b) Explain why he hears the loudest noise.

✎ _____ *(1 mark)* ☐

Q7b

c) The drummer hits the drum skin with his drumstick.

What happens to the drum skin when it makes a sound?

✎ _____ *(1 mark)* ☐

Q7c

d) The drummer has different sizes of drums.

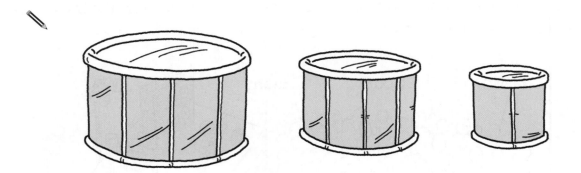

Draw a circle around the drum that produces a higher pitched sound.

(1 mark)

e) Which of the following best describes the **pitch** of a sound?
Tick **ONE** box.

Loud or quiet sounds ☐

High or low sounds ☐

Long or short notes ☐

(1 mark)

(Total 5 marks)

Milk from Milk Powder

8 Instant milk powder is useful when fresh milk is not available.

a) How is instant milk powder made into liquid milk?

✎ _____

_____ (1 mark)

b) i Instant milk powder is made by spraying skimmed milk onto heated rollers. The milk powder can be scraped off the rollers.

What change happens on the rollers?

✎ _____

_____ (1 mark)

ii Is the change that takes place on the rollers reversible or non-reversible? Explain your answer.

✎ _____

_____

_____ (1 mark)

(Total 3 marks)

END OF TEST

Set

B

KEY STAGE 2
Levels 3–5

Test Paper 1

Science

Test Paper 1

Test Paper 1

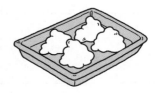

Instructions:

- find a quiet place where you can sit down and complete the test paper undisturbed

- make sure you have all the necessary equipment to complete the test paper

- read the questions carefully

- answer all the questions in this test paper

- go through and check your answers when you have finished the test paper

✎ This pencil shows where you will have to put your answer. Sometimes you may have to draw the answer instead of writing one.

Time:

This test paper is **45 minutes** long.

Note to Parents:

Check how your child has done against the Answers and Mark Scheme on pages 97–104.

Page	37	39	41	43	45	47	49	51	Max. Mark	**Actual Mark**
Score	....	....	....	....	....	....	....	....	40	....

First name ....

Last name ....

Watering Plants

1 Adam and Becky are trying to find out if plants need water to grow and, if so, how much water they need to grow.

Adam has four plants. He adds different amounts of water to each plant every day.

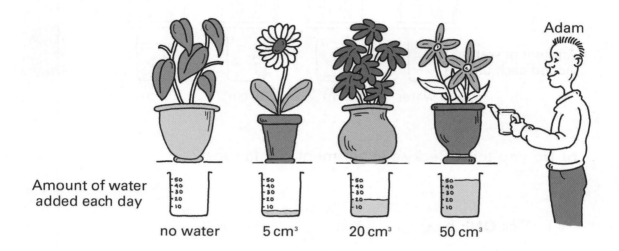

Amount of water added each day

no water   5 cm³   20 cm³   50 cm³

Adam

Adam measures the height of the plants every week.

a) Why does Adam's teacher think this is not a fair test?

✎ _____

_____ *(1 mark)*

Q1a

Becky has ten plants in each tray.

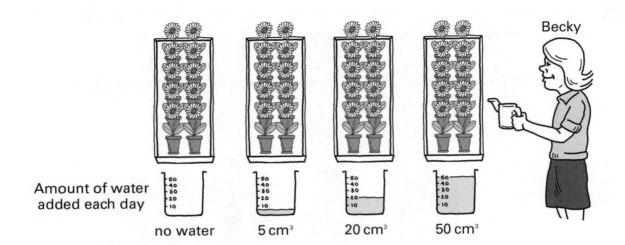

Amount of water added each day

no water   5 cm³   20 cm³   50 cm³

b) Do you think Becky's experiment is a fair test?

i   Tick **ONE** box.   Yes ☐   No ☐

ii   Give a reason for your answer.

_____

_____ *(1 mark)*

Here are their results.

Adam's results

Amount of water (cm³)	Height of plants (cm)			
	at start	week 1	week 2	week 3
0	10	dead	dead	dead
5	6	7		9
20	4	dead	dead	dead
50	6	6	dead	dead

Adam forgot to write down the height for 5 cm³ of water for week 2.

c) **Complete the table to show what the reading might have been.** *(1 mark)*

Q1c

Becky's results

Amount of water (cm³)	Average height of plants (cm)			
	at start	week 1	week 2	week 3
0	5	dead	dead	dead
5	5	6	7	8.5
20	5	8	10	11
50	5	5	dead	dead

subtotal

d) Becky starts to draw a line graph of the height of plants with 20 cm³ of water.

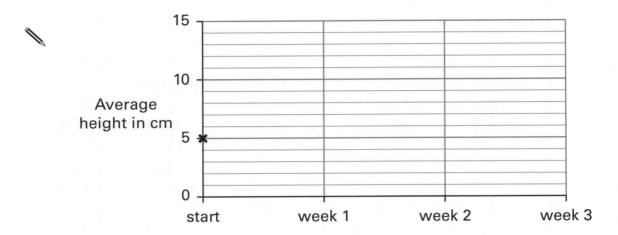

i   Finish plotting the points.
The first one has been done for you.

(2 marks)

Q1d

ii   Draw a line through the points.

(1 mark)

Q1d

e) Adam makes a conclusion for his results:

Plants need 5 cm³ of water for healthy growth.

Becky says:

You do not have enough information to support your conclusion.

i   Who do you agree with? Tick ONE box.

Agree with Adam ☐   Agree with Becky ☐

ii Suggest why you agreed with either Adam or Becky.

_____

_____ (1 mark)

f) Write a conclusion for Becky's results.

_____

_____

_____ (2 marks)

(Total 9 marks)

Purifying Rock Salt

2 Jemima has some crushed rock salt. She looks at a sample with a hand lens.

a) i   What will she see?

✎ _____

_____ *(1 mark)*

ii Why is this?

✎ _____

_____ *(1 mark)*

She adds some of the rock salt to water and she stirs the mixture.

b) Why does this separate the salt from the other impurities?

✎ _____

_____ *(2 marks)*

c) i Draw a diagram showing how she could separate the mixture. *(1 mark)*

Label your diagram.

ii What is the name of this process?

_____ *(1 mark)*

d) Jemima wants to recover the pure salt.

i Put a ring around the best word to describe the method
she uses. *(1 mark)*

burning   condensing   evaporating   melting

ii Draw a diagram showing how she could recover the salt. *(1 mark)*

Q2di

Label your diagram.

e) i What would Jemima see if she looked at the salt she had recovered through a hand lens?

_____ *(1 mark)*

Q2e

ii Why is this?

_____

_____ *(1 mark)*

Q2e

(Total 10 marks)

Forces

3 Tim is measuring the force needed to pull his shoe across a wooden floor. He attaches a force meter to his shoe and pulls.

The reading on the force meter is 4**N**.

a) Tick **ONE** box to show what N stands for.

Newton ☐   **Nitrogen** ☐   **Nought** ☐   *(1 mark)* ☐

Q3a

b) Tim and Nick want to find out if different floor surfaces will affect the force needed to pull the shoe.

What is the **ONE** factor they should change as they carry out their investigation?

_____*(1 mark)* ☐

Q3b

c) Name **ONE** of the factors they should keep the same to make their investigation fair.

_____*(1 mark)* ☐

Q3c

subtotal

d) They carry out their investigation three times. Here are their results.

Force needed to pull the shoe

Floor surface	Force (N)		
	test 1	test 2	test 3
carpet	12	12	13
wood	9	4	10
vinyl	3	4	3

i   For which floor surface does one of the results seem unlikely?

_____ *(1 mark)*

Q3

ii Which floor surface needed the most force to move the shoe?

_____ *(1 mark)*

Q3

e) The picture shows Tim pulling the shoe.

Label the arrows on the picture to say what **forces** they show.
One force has been labelled for you.

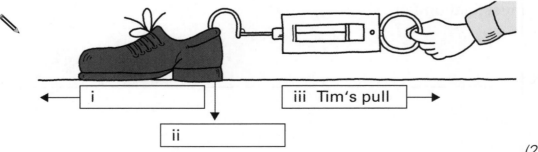

(2 marks)

Q3

(Total 7 marks)

Baking Bread

4 A baker is making bread. He mixes the ingredients including flour, water and yeast. He forms a dough. He leaves this in a warm place for a few hours.

a) i What happens to the dough when it is left?

_____ (1 mark)

ii Why is this important?

_____

_____ (1 mark)

b) i What is done to the dough to turn it into the final loaf of bread?

_____

_____ (1 mark)

ii How does the dough change during this process?

_____

_____ (1 mark)

(Total 4 marks)

The Dentist

5 Sally visits her dentist.

a) The dentist removes one of Sally's milk teeth. The dentist tells Sally there will not be a gap in her teeth for long.

Why is this?

✎ _____

_____ *(1 mark)*

b) The dentist tells Sally about the different types of teeth and the job they do.

Draw THREE lines to match each type of tooth to the job it does.

✎ **Type of tooth**   **Job it does**

| incisor | | tearing food |

| canine | | cutting food |

| molar | | chewing food | *(2 marks)*

c) The dentist tells Sally that some foods will damage her teeth.

Tick **TWO** boxes to show which foods will damage teeth.

apples ☐

carrots ☐

chocolates ☐

sweets ☐

(2 marks) ☐
Q5c

(Total 5 marks)

Sundials

6 Sundials have been used to find the time for hundreds of years.

a) How does a sundial use light from the Sun to show the time?

✎ _____

_____ *(2 marks)*

Q6

b) What is the time shown on this sundial?

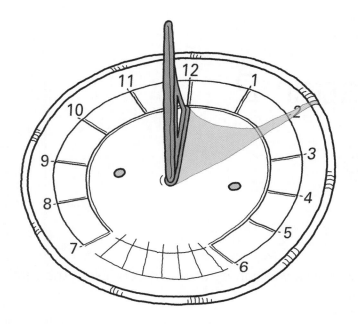

✏ _____ (1 mark)

c) At 12:00 noon in the summer, the Sun is ...

Tick **TWO** boxes.

✏ **due south.** ☐

  due north. ☐

  high in the sky. ☐

  low in the sky. ☐   (2 marks)

(Total 5 marks)

END OF TEST

Set

B

page 52

KEY STAGE 2
Levels 3–5

Test Paper 2

Science

Test Paper 2

Test Paper 2

Instructions:

- find a quiet place where you can sit down and complete the test paper undisturbed

- make sure you have all the necessary equipment to complete the test paper

- read the questions carefully

- answer all the questions in this test paper

- go through and check your answers when you have finished the test paper

✏️ This pencil shows where you will have to put your answer. Sometimes you may have to draw the answer instead of writing one.

Time:

This test paper is **45 minutes** long.

Note to Parents:

Check how your child has done against the Answers and Mark Scheme on pages 97–104.

Page	53	55	57	59	61	63	65	66	Max. Mark	**Actual Mark**
Score	....	....	....	....	....	....	....	....	40	....

First name _____

Last name _____

Looking around the Kitchen

1 Jo collects a number of things from the kitchen.

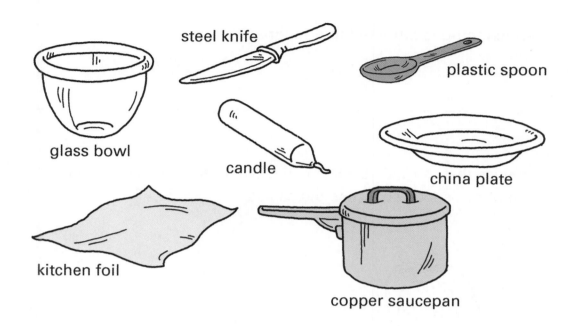

a) Which **THREE** things are made of metal?

✎ _____

_____

_____ *(2 marks)*

b) Which thing is transparent?

✎ _____ *(1 mark)*

c) Why is copper a good material to use for making saucepans?

✎ _____ (1 mark)

d) Which thing is attracted to a magnet?

✎ _____ (1 mark)

e) Jo finds that the knife scratches the candle and the plastic spoon.
   The plastic spoon scratches the candle.

Put these three things in order of hardness. Put the softest one first.

✎   softest   _____

_____

hardest   _____   (2 marks)

(Total 7 marks)

The Heart

2 a) **On the diagram** mark the position of the heart with the letter **H**.

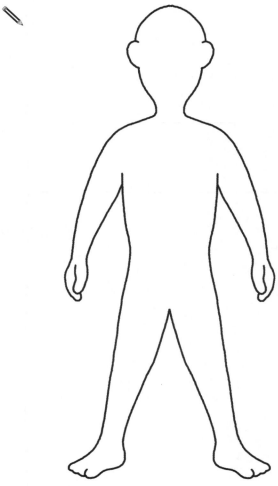

(1 mark)

b) Which part of the body protects the heart? Tick **ONE** box.

hair ☐   **skin** ☐   **skull** ☐   **ribs** ☐   *(1 mark)*

c) Which blood vessels take blood away from the heart? Circle **ONE** word.

arteries   **capillaries**   **veins**   *(1 mark)*

d) Which blood vessels take blood to the heart? Circle **ONE** word.

    arteries   **capillaries**   **veins**   *(1 mark)*

Q2d

e) What is the job of the heart?

_____

_____ *(2 marks)*

Q2e

(Total 6 marks)

Cooling Curves

3 Mrs Brown is showing Class 6 an experiment. She has a glass beaker containing very hot water. She puts a temperature probe into the water. She covers the beaker with a lid.

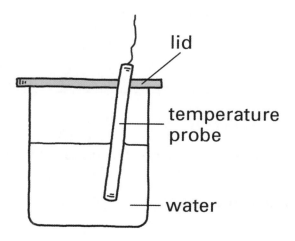

a) What could she use if she did not have a temperature probe?

✎ _____ *(1 mark)*

Q3a

The computer takes the temperature of the water every 15 seconds and draws a graph of the results.

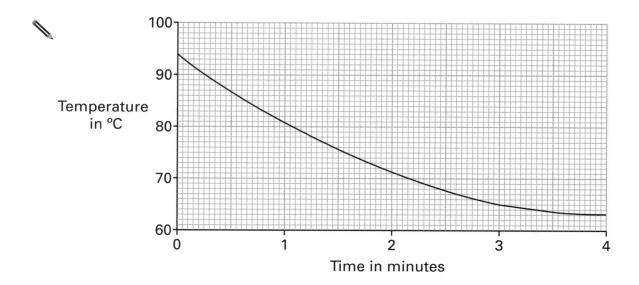

b) What was the starting temperature of the water in the beaker?

✎ _____ *(1 mark)*

c) What was the temperature after 3 minutes?

✎ _____ *(1 mark)*

d) Sam says that the temperature may not be the same throughout the water.

What could Mrs Brown do to make sure it is?

✎ _____ *(1 mark)*

e) Mrs Brown does the experiment again, wrapping an insulator around the beaker.

On the grid on page 57, sketch the graph you would expect the computer to show. *(2 marks)*

f) The class are then set a problem:

'How would they find out whether felt is an insulator?'

They keep the beaker the same.

Write down TWO other things they should keep the same.

✎ _____

_____ *(2 marks)*

(Total 8 marks)

Motors

4 Kerry makes this circuit. The motor is turning a fan.

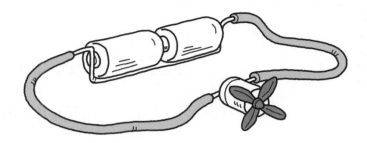

a) Describe how the motor is turning the fan in each of the circuits below. Choose words from this list. You can use them once, more than once or not at all.

not turning   **turning fast**   **turning slowly**

The first one has been done for you.

(3 marks)

A

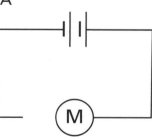

✎ _____not turning_____

B

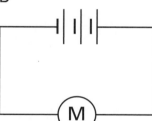

✎ _____

C

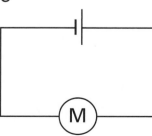

D

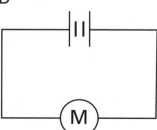

✎ _____   ✎ _____

subtotal

b) Why is the motor not turning in Circuit A?

_____

_____ (1 mark)

Q4b

(Total 4 marks)

Making Bread

5 Tom's class are going to make bread. Mr Smith shows them what to do. The pictures show how he makes the bread.

1 Collect ingredients

2 Mix together

3 Leave in a warm place

4 Ready to be baked

a) Before they start, all the children have to wash their hands.

Why is this?

_____

_____ *(1 mark)*

Q5a

subtotal

b) Tom makes his bread. He forgets to leave it in a warm place.

Tick **ONE** box to show the effect this will have on his bread.

His bread will rise faster. ☐

His bread will rise very slowly. ☐

His bread will not rise at all. ☐

There will be no effect on his bread. ☐

(1 mark)

Q5b

c) Why does sugar need to be added to the mixture?

✎ _____

_____ *(1 mark)*

Q5c

d) Jane makes her bread. She forgets to add the yeast.

Describe how Jane's bread will look by stage 4 on page 61.

✎ _____

_____ *(1 mark)*

Q5

e) Yeast is a microbe.

Tick **TWO** boxes to show which foods are made by using microbes.

cheese ☐

chocolate ☐

meat ☐

potatoes ☐

yoghurt ☐ (2 marks) ☐

(Total 6 marks)

Bike Ride

6 Rachael rides her bike early in the morning on a long journey.
The Sun is low in the sky.

East

Sun

West

puddle

a) Rachael can see a puddle on the road.

On the diagram draw a line to show how Rachael can see the puddle.
Label your line with a **P**.

(2 marks)

QE

b) During her bike ride, the position of the Sun in the sky changes.

Draw a line on the same diagram that shows the movement of the Sun
during the day. Label the line **S**. Mark the position of the Sun at midday.

(2 marks)

QE

(Total 4 marks)

Birthday Party

7 It is Steven's birthday. Steven looks at the candles on his birthday cake.

a) The candles give out light.

   Circle **TWO** other objects that give out light.

   ✎   **lit torch bulb**   **Moon**   **satellite**   **Sun**   *(1 mark)*   □ Q7a

b) Steven's friends sing 'Happy Birthday'.

   Steven's mum walks away from the children and leaves the room.

   What happens to the sound Steven's mum hears as she goes further away from the children?

   ✎ _____ *(1 mark)*   □ Q7b

c) Steven's mum shuts the wooden door. She can still hear the children singing. One material the sound is travelling through is air.

   Name **ONE** other material the sound is travelling through for Steven's mum to hear it.

   ✎ _____ *(1 mark)*

d) Steven is holding a balloon. The balloon is filled with helium.

   What **TWO** things are pulling the balloon down?

   ✎ _____

   _____ *(2 marks)*

(Total 5 marks)

END OF TEST

Test Paper 1

Instructions:

- find a quiet place where you can sit down and complete the test paper undisturbed
- make sure you have all the necessary equipment to complete the test paper
- read the questions carefully
- answer all the questions in this test paper
- go through and check your answers when you have finished the test paper

✎ This pencil shows where you will have to put your answer. Sometimes you may have to draw the answer instead of writing one.

Time:

This test paper is **45 minutes** long.

Note to Parents:

Check how your child has done against the Answers and Mark Scheme on pages 97–104.

Page	69	71	73	75	77	79	81	82	Max. Mark	**Actual Mark**
Score	....	....	....	....	....	....	....	....	40	....

First name   _____

Last name   _____

Football

1 Alex is practising his football skills. He is kicking the ball into the goal.

a) Which diagram shows the force acting on the ball as it hits the net?

   Draw a circle around the correct diagram.

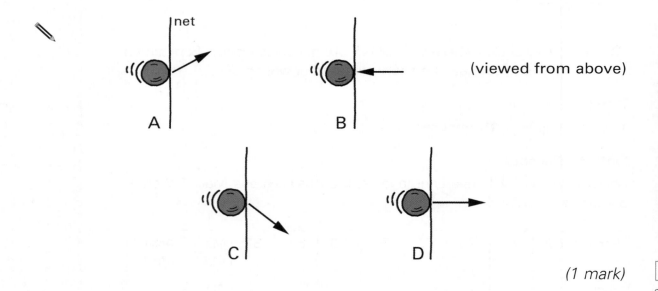

(1 mark)

b) Tick **TWO** boxes that show **two** things that change when the ball
   bounces off the net.

   The colour of the net ☐   **The shape of the net** ☐

   The colour of the ball ☐   **The direction of the ball** ☐   *(2 marks)*

Alex kicks the ball across the football pitch. The ball does not travel very far.

Next time, Alex kicks the ball very hard.

c) **What happens to the distance the ball travels on this second kick, compared to the first kick?**

✎ _____

_____ *(1 mark)*

Q1c

subtotal

Alex kicks the ball up into the air.

d) What force makes the ball return to the ground?

✎ _____ (1 mark)

(Total 5 marks)

Reaction with a Fizz

2   Class 6 watch an experiment. Mr Smith drops a spoonful of liver salts into a beaker of cold water and stirs the solution.

They see the mixture fizz and a colourless gas escapes from the beaker. Then he drops a spoonful of salt into another beaker of cold water and stirs the solution. Mr Smith tells them that the change with liver salts is **not** reversible but the change with salt is **reversible**.

a) Can they get the liver salts and the salt back from the final solutions?

liver salts _____

salt _____ *(1 mark)*   Q2a

b) Which of the following suggests that the change with liver salts is not reversible? Tick **ONE** box.

Mr Smith stirs the mixture. ☐   **The mixture fizzes.** ☐

The solution left is colourless. ☐   **The change is quick.** ☐   *(1 mark)*   Q2b

c) Mr Smith does the experiment again. This time he weighs the beaker of water and the solid before, and the solution afterwards.

i   How would you expect the mass to change when liver salts are added to water?

✎ _____ (1 mark)

Why is this?

✎ _____

_____ (1 mark)

ii How would you expect the mass to change when salt is added to water?

✎ _____ (1 mark)

Why is this?

✎ _____

_____ (1 mark)

d) Why is it important that liver salts are sold in a tin with a tight lid, rather than in a cardboard box?

_____

_____ (1 mark)

(Total 7 marks)

Bones and Muscles

3 Ben and Sarah are learning about bones.

a) Write a label in each box. Use words from this list.

ribs   **skull**   **spine**

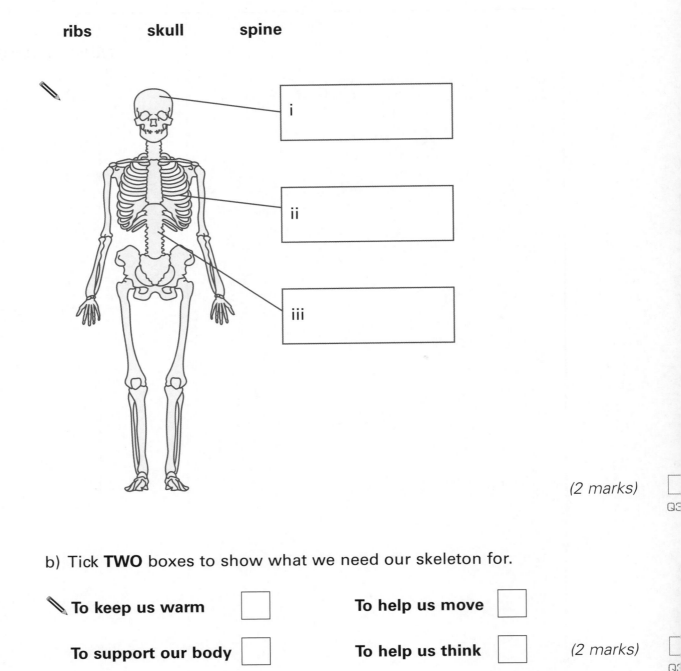

i

ii

iii

(2 marks)

b) Tick **TWO** boxes to show what we need our skeleton for.

To keep us warm ☐   **To help us move** ☐

To support our body ☐   **To help us think** ☐   *(2 marks)*

c) Ben has some ideas about his skeleton.

Write **true** or **false** below each idea.

My muscles are attached to my bones.

_____

My bones are hard and strong.

_____

My skeleton grows as I grow.

_____

My bones can bend in the middle so I can move.

_____

(3 marks)

Q3c

d) Ben is playing football. Sarah is sitting down watching him. Ben says his muscles are tired. Sarah says her muscles are not tired.

Why are Ben's muscles tired?

_____

_____ *(1 mark)*

Q3d

(Total 8 marks)

subtotal

Mirrors

4 Class 5B are investigating mirrors. Jane uses her mirror to look at a spot on her chin.

a) **On the diagram** draw one arrowhead on each of the lines **A** and **B** to show how the light travels.

(2 marks)

b) Which word describes what happens to the light at the mirror? Circle your choice.

deflection   **inflection**   **reflection**   **refraction**

(1 mark)

c) Jane and Laura are looking into a mirror, but there is a book between them.

Jane shines a torch onto the mirror so that Laura can see the torch.

On the diagram draw lines to show how Laura can see the torch. *(2 marks)*

Q4c

d) Jane uses a piece of paper instead of the mirror.

Why can Laura not see the torch?

_____

_____ *(1 mark)*

Q4d

(Total 6 marks)

Earth, Sun and Moon

5   Mrs Smiles shows Class 5C a model of the Earth, Sun and Moon.
She uses a lamp for the Sun and a football for the Earth.

Sun

Earth

a) **On the diagram** shade the part of the Earth that is in darkness.   *(1 mark)*

b) Mrs Smiles wants to show the class how day becomes night.

What should Mrs Smiles do to show this?

Write below or draw on the diagram.

_____ *(1 mark)*

Q5

c) Mrs Smiles wants to show the class the position of the Moon.

What could she use for the Moon?

_____ (1 mark)

Q5c

d) **On the diagram** on page 78 draw the Moon in its
correct position. (1 mark)

Q5d

(Total 4 marks)

subtotal

Life Cycle of a Plant

6 The picture shows a growing plant.

The diagram shows the life cycle of a flowering plant.

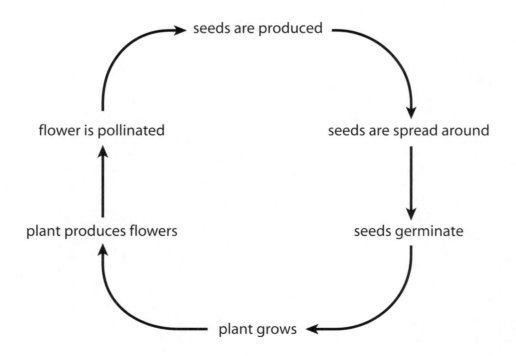

a) Tick the **TWO** boxes that show how seeds can be spread around. *(2 marks)*

animals ☐ crawl ☐ walk ☐ wind ☐

b) What happens when seeds germinate?

_____

_____ *(1 mark)*

c) Tick **TWO** boxes to show **two** conditions needed for germination. *(2 marks)*

gravity ☐ light ☐ moisture ☐ warmth ☐ wind ☐

d) Which stage of the life cycle is often carried out by insects?

_____ *(1 mark)*

(Total 6 marks)

Water Cycle

7 The diagram shows the water cycle.

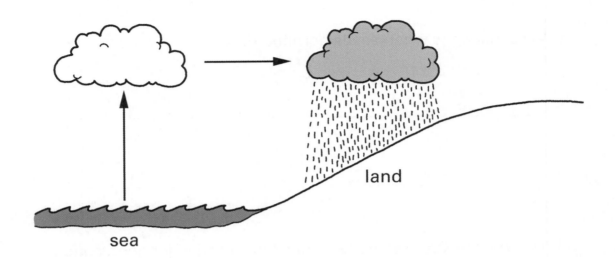

Finish the explanation of the water cycle. Use words from this list in your answer.

boils   clouds   condenses   evaporates   freezes   vapour

✎ Water falls from the skies as rain when the clouds cool and the water vapour

_____. The rain water runs into streams and

finally into the sea. The water in the sea _____

to form water _____. This produces

_____ and the cycle continues.

(Total 4 marks)

END OF TEST

Set C

KEY STAGE 2
Levels 3–5

Test Paper 2

Science

Test Paper 2

Test Paper 2

Instructions:

- find a quiet place where you can sit down and complete the test paper undisturbed
- make sure you have all the necessary equipment to complete the test paper
- read the questions carefully
- answer all the questions in this test paper
- go through and check your answers when you have finished the test paper

 This pencil shows where you will have to put your answer. Sometimes you may have to draw the answer instead of writing one.

Time:

This test paper is **45 minutes** long.

Note to Parents:

Check how your child has done against the Answers and Mark Scheme on pages 97–104.

Page	85	87	89	91	93	95	96	Max. Mark	**Actual Mark**
Score	....	....	....	....	....	....	....	40	....

First name ....

Last name ....

A Walk in the Country

1 Lee goes for a walk in the country.

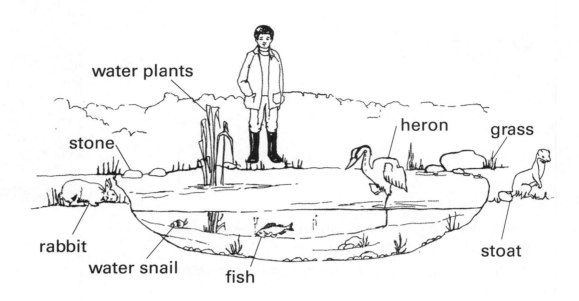

a) Lee can see different animals living in different habitats.

Finish the table by writing the name of an animal that lives in the habitat.

Habitat	Animal
pond	
field	

(2 marks)

b) Finish the table by writing the name of **ONE** living thing and **ONE** non-living thing.

Living thing	Non-living thing

(1 mark)

c) Write down **TWO** things that living things can do which non-living things cannot do.

✎ _____

_____ *(2 marks)*

d) Lee can see the water snails eating the water plants. He knows that fish eat water snails.

Finish the food chain. The last part has been done for you.

✎
			heron

(1 mark)

e) Finish the table by writing the name of **ONE** thing in each column.

✎

Producer	Prey	Predator

(3 marks)

(Total 9 marks)

Our Solar System

2   The Sun, the Earth and the Moon are three objects in our Solar System.

a) **Which object is the same shape as the Earth?** Tick **ONE** box.

✎ **A 2p coin** ☐

A football ☐

A 50p coin ☐

A breakfast cereal box ☐   *(1 mark)*   ☐

Q2a

b) Adam has some ideas about the Sun, Earth and Moon.

Write **true** or **false** below each idea.

✎

1   The Sun and the Moon both go around the Earth.
_____

2   The Earth and the Moon both go around the Sun.
_____

3   It takes one year for the Earth to orbit the Sun.
_____

(2 marks)   ☐

Q2

The picture shows the position of the Sun early in the morning in summer.

c) **On the diagram** draw the position of the Sun at midday. Label this with an **M**.

(1 mark)

Q2c

d) **On the diagram** draw the position of the Sun in the evening, before sunset. Label this with an **E**.

(1 mark)

Q2d

(Total 5 marks)

subtotal

Melting Ice

3 Kim takes a glass out of the refrigerator. It has been in there some time. It contains cubes of ice floating in water.

ice

water

a) The ice cubes float in water.

   What does that tell you about ice?

   ✎ _____ *(1 mark)*

b) Kim measures the temperature of the mixture of ice and water.

   i   **Write down the name of the piece of apparatus she uses.**

   ✎ _____ *(1 mark)*

   ii **Draw a ring around the likely temperature of ice and water.**

   ✎   **–10°C**   **0°C**   **10°C**   **20°C**   *(1 mark)*

c) She leaves the glass on the work surface until the ice has just turned to water.

   i   Is ice turning to water a reversible or a non-reversible change? Explain your answer.

      _____

      _____ *(1 mark)*

   ii What name is given to the change from ice to water?

      _____ *(1 mark)*

   iii The outside of the glass standing on the work surface goes misty. Why is this?

      _____

      _____ *(2 marks)*

d) Kim takes another glass containing ice and water out of the refrigerator. She adds salt to the mixture.

   What happens to the temperature of the mixture?

      _____ *(1 mark)*

(Total 8 marks)

Cress Seeds

4 Emily and Lucy are growing cress plants. They put them in three different places.

in a greenhouse   in a dark, warm cupboard   on a windowsill

a) Emily says this was not a fair test because they forgot to water the plants in the cupboard.

Tick **TWO** boxes to show two other things that made this an unfair test.

They were left for the same length of time.   ☐

It was warmer in the greenhouse.   ☐

Different cress seeds were used to grow the plants.   ☐

The same containers were used.   ☐

The seeds were planted in the same type of soil.   ☐   *(2 marks)*   ☐
Q4

b) Lucy makes lots of conclusions for this experiment.

For each of Lucy's conclusions tick **ONE** box.

	True	False	Can't tell
The plants in the cupboard died because they had no light.	☐	☐	☐
The plants on the windowsill grew towards the light.	☐	☐	☐
Warmth is needed for plants to grow.	☐	☐	☐
The plants in the greenhouse died.	☐	☐	☐

(4 marks) ☐
Q4b

c) Finish the sentence. Choose your word from this list.

flowers   **leaves**   **roots**   **stems**

Plants take in water through their _____ *(1 mark)* ☐
Q4c

(Total 7 marks)

subtotal

Types of Sugar

5 Granulated sugar, caster sugar and icing sugar are three types of sugar you might have in your kitchen. Granulated sugar has larger crystals than caster sugar. Icing sugar is a fine powder.

Tony adds one tablespoonful of granulated sugar to 100 cm³ of water and stirs it until he can no longer see the sugar. He repeats the experiment twice more.

Then he carries out the whole experiment using icing sugar and caster sugar.

His results are shown in the table.

Type of sugar	Time for sugar to disappear in seconds		
	1st experiment	2nd experiment	3rd experiment
granulated	45	50	52
icing	20	12	22
caster	32	34	35

a) Which word best describes what happens when sugar is added to water and it can no longer be seen?

   Put a ring around the best word.

   ✎   **dissolve**   **evaporate**   **melt**   *(1 mark)*

b) Why did Tony test each sugar three times?

   ✎ _____

   _____ *(1 mark)*

c) Tony looks at his results and thinks that one result is wrong.

   Which result is wrong?

   ✎ _____ *(1 mark)*

d) **How does the size of the sugar grains affect the time for the sugar to dissolve?**

   ✎ _____

   _____ *(2 marks)*

e) Tony has used the same amount of sugar and the same amount of water each time.

   Suggest one other thing that might affect the results.

   ✎ _____ *(1 mark)*

f) **Suggest one other thing Tony could do to make granulated sugar dissolve faster.**

   ✎ _____

   _____ *(1 mark)*

(Total 7 marks)

Stretching Elastic Bands

6 Mohammed is experimenting with elastic bands and masses. He puts a mass onto the hanger and records the length of the elastic band. Mohammed adds more masses.

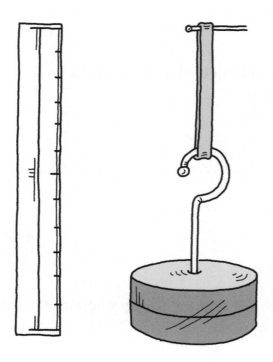

a) What could happen that makes this experiment unsafe?

_____

_____ *(1 mark)*

Mohammed drew a line graph of his results.

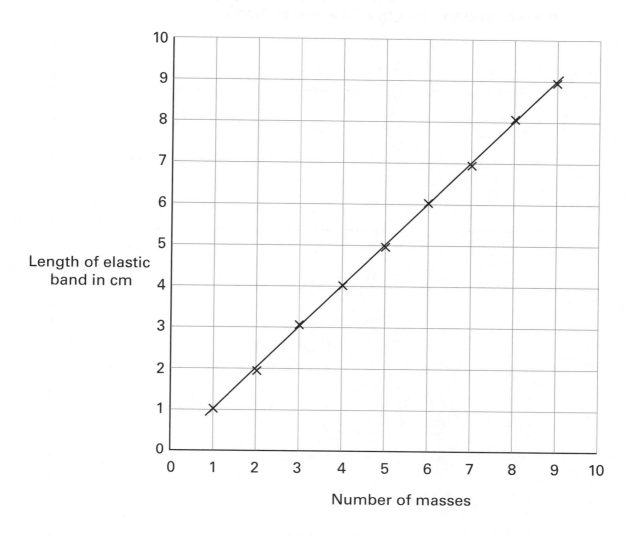

b) What is the length of the elastic band when four masses are added?

✎ _____ cm

(1 mark)

c) Predict the length of the elastic band when ten masses are added.

✎ _____ cm

(1 mark)

subtotal

d) Describe what Mohammed's graph tells him about the **number of masses** and **the length of the elastic band**.

_____

_____

_____ *(1 mark)*

(Total 4 marks)

Q6d

END OF TEST

Answers and Mark Scheme

Set A Test Paper 1

1 a) Light passes through it or you can see
       through it   *(1 mark)*
       Note to parent *Your child should also know that*
       opaque is the opposite of transparent. You cannot
       see through an opaque block.
    b) iron   *(1 mark)*
    c) plasticine   *(1 mark)*
    d) polystyrene   *(1 mark)*
       wood   *(1 mark)*
       Note to parent *Polystyrene and wood have*
       a lower density than water and this is why
       they float.
    e) polystyrene, wood, iron   *(2 marks)*
       Note to parent *Award 1 mark if polystyrene is*
       before wood in the list, and 1 mark if wood is
       before iron.
    f) i To insulate the kitchen **or** to keep the
          kitchen warmer   *(1 mark)*
       ii Low density   *(1 mark)*
          Very good heat insulator   *(1 mark)*
                                      Total 10 marks

2 a) For food   *(1 mark)*
       Note to parent *Most children forget that plants*
       are grown for food. They are used to food coming
       from the supermarket with little consideration of
       where it came from before that. Most children's
       experience of plants growing will be the flowers in
       their garden at home.
    b) carrots
       rabbits
       fox   *(2 marks)*
       Carrots anywhere before rabbits – 1 mark
       Rabbits anywhere before fox – 1 mark
    c) fox   *(1 mark)*
    d) rabbits will have less food
       or rabbits will need to go somewhere else
       for food   *(1 mark)*
                                       Total 5 marks

3 a) Any two from:
       Movement of air or wind
       High temperature
       Air is dry, i.e. has low humidity   *(2 marks)*
    b) evaporating   *(1 mark)*
    c) At night the temperature falls   *(1 mark)*
       Water vapour in the air condenses
       in the clothes   *(1 mark)*
       Note to parent *It is important that your child uses*
       the word 'condenses' to represent the change
       from vapour (gas) to liquid.
                                       Total 5 marks

4 a) Arrow pointing upwards from paper clip
       to magnet   *(1 mark)*
    b)

                                           (2 marks)
       Allow 1 mark for each bar drawn correctly
       Note to parent *Your child should be able to draw*
       bar charts and interpret them. Check that your
       child has drawn the top of each bar horizontally.
    c) Slab magnet   *(1 mark)*
    d) It picks up the most paper clips   *(1 mark)*
                                       Total 5 marks

5 a) 80 (beats per minute)   *(1 mark)*
    b) 68 (beats per minute)   *(1 mark)*
       Note to parent *Part b) is harder because the child*
       needs to work out the scale on the vertical axis
       before working out the answer. Working out the
       scale on the axis is a skill that needs practice. In
       this case each small square represents 2 beats
       per minute.
    c) The pulse rate goes up   *(1 mark)*
    d) The body needs more oxygen   *(1 mark)*
       So the heart is pumping blood around
       the body faster   *(1 mark)*
    e) 6–8 (minutes)   *(1 mark)*
                                       Total 6 marks

6 a) 35 (°C)   *(1 mark)*
    b) Cup C   *(1 mark)*
    c) 25 (°C)   *(1 mark)*
       Note to parent *Parts a) and c) are taken from the*
       graph. In b) the cup that cools fastest will be the
       one where the temperature falls fastest, i.e.
       the steepest.
    d) thermal insulator   *(1 mark)*
       Note to parent *Your child needs to understand*
       that in science the words 'insulator' and
       'conductor' can be applied to electricity and to
       energy loss. Look at a piece of electrical wire and
       discuss which materials are electrical conductors

and which are insulators. Look at examples of thermal insulation and conduction, e.g. metal and plastic saucepan handles.

e) Put a lid over the cup *(1 mark)*

Total 5 marks

7 a)

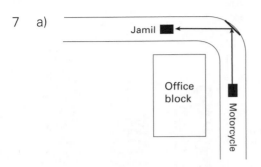

Mirror drawn at correct angle *(1 mark)*
Light ray from mirror to Jamil must be at right angles to ray from motorcycle to mirror *(1 mark)*

b) The office block is between Jamil and the motorcycle *(1 mark)*

Note to parent *Your child should know that light rays travel in straight lines. It is important that a ruler is used to draw light rays.*

c) reflects *(1 mark)*

Total 4 marks

Set A Test Paper 2

1 a)

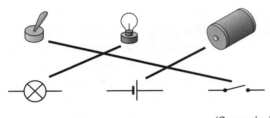

(2 marks)

3 correct – 2 marks
1 or 2 correct – 1 mark

b)

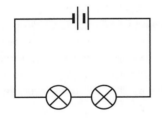

(1 mark)

c) dimmer **or** less bright *(1 mark)*

d) i

Material	Bulbs light up	Bulbs do not light up
plastic		✓
iron	✓	

(1 mark)

Both must be correct for 1 mark

ii conductor *(1 mark)*
insulator *(1 mark)*

Total 7 marks

2 a) Line drawn from football to Sun
Line drawn from pea to Earth
Line drawn from small bead to Moon
All 3 correct *(1 mark)*

b) Jane walks around Becky in a circle

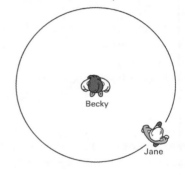

(1 mark)

c) 1 true
2 false
3 true *(2 marks)*
All 3 correct – 2 marks
2 correct – 1 mark

Total 4 marks

3 a)

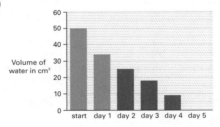

(2 marks)

All correct – 2 marks
2 or 3 correct – 1 mark

b) 2 days *(1 mark)*

Note to parent *This is another opportunity for your child to practise bar charts like the one in Set A Test Paper 1, page 13.*

c) petrol   water   motor oil *(2 marks)*
Petrol anywhere before water – 1 mark
Water anywhere before motor oil – 1 mark

Total 5 marks

4 a) apple (1 mark)
     lettuce (1 mark)
   b) Plants have less room for roots
      to grow (1 mark)
      Water is taken in through the roots (1 mark)
   c) i thin or spindly (1 mark)
         pale leaves (1 mark)
      Note to parent *It is important that children*
      understand the difference between 'describe'
      and 'explain'. This question asks for a
      description of what they can see.
      ii Lack of light (1 mark)
                              Total 7 marks

5 a) Sieve (1 mark)
      Note to parent *Do not worry if the spelling is not*
      correct. Award the mark if it sounds right.
   b) Same volume (amount) of water
      Same mass (amount) of soil (2 marks)
      Note to parent *Try to get your child not to use*
      the word 'amount' but a more scientific
      alternative. But award the mark for 'amount'
      this time.
   c) Sandy (no mark)
      The particles of sand pack together with
      plenty of spaces between them (because
      they are large particles). The water can
      move through these spaces. (1 mark)
      Note to parent *This answer may be helped by*
      drawing two diagrams – one with large particles
      packed together and one with small particles. You
      can then clearly see the bigger gaps through
      which water will pass.
                              Total 4 marks

6 a) fish **and** duck (1 mark)
   b) Does the animal have more than
      two legs? (1 mark)
      Note to parent *When attempting questions about*
      using keys it is important that children read all of
      the information in the key. The temptation is to
      read just to the part needed. This will make it
      more difficult to answer the question.
   c) fish (1 mark)
   d) worm (1 mark)
   e) To help identify animals (1 mark)
                              Total 5 marks

7 a) Liam (1 mark)
   b) He is closest to the source of
      the sound (1 mark)
   c) It vibrates (1 mark)
      Note to parent *The word 'vibrate' is an important*
      scientific word. Demonstrate the vibration of a
      ruler held over the edge of a table.
   d) Smallest drum (1 mark)
   e) High or low sounds (1 mark)
      Note to parent *The word 'pitch' is a property of*
      sound determined by its frequency. High pitch
      sounds are associated with high frequencies.
                              Total 5 marks

8 a) By adding water (1 mark)
   b) i Water evaporates or boils (1 mark)
      ii Reversible change (no mark)
         In part a) it was shown that the reverse
         step can take place (1 mark)
      Note to parent *The question is just testing your*
      child's understanding of the words 'reversible' and
      'non-reversible'.
                              Total 3 marks

Set B Test Paper 1

1 a) Different plants
      or different size pots (1 mark)
   b) i Yes (no mark)
      ii She used the same plants
         or the same trays (1 mark)
   c) 8 (1 mark)
   d) i–ii

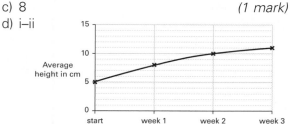

      All 3 points plotted correctly – 2 marks
      1 or 2 points plotted correctly – 1 mark
      ii Smooth curve through most of
         the points (1 mark)

   e) i Agree with Adam or Becky (no mark)
      ii Any one from:
         If agreed with Adam – 5 cm³ of water
         was the only plant to grow; Plants with
         no water, 20 cm³ and 50 cm³ of water
         died. If agreed with Becky – Only one
         plant was used for each amount of water
         and the one plant might die (1 mark)
      Note to parent *This question is attempting to*
      test children's understanding of practical skills.
      The answer ideally needs to show an awareness
      that more than one plant is needed in case one
      dies. More results are needed for a conclusion.
   f) Plants need water to grow, (1 mark)
      but not too much water (1 mark)
                              Total 9 marks

2 a) i   She sees bits of different colours *(1 mark)*
      ii Rock salt is a mixture of substances,
          not one pure substance *(1 mark)*
   b) The salt dissolves *(1 mark)*
      The impurities do not dissolve *(1 mark)*
   c) i

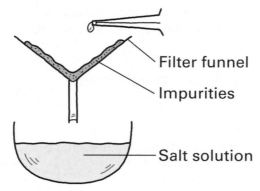

Filter funnel

Impurities

Salt solution

(1 mark)

      ii Filtration (or filtering) *(1 mark)*
   d) i   evaporating *(1 mark)*
      ii

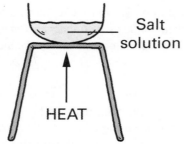

Salt solution

HEAT

(1 mark)

   e) i   All the crystals look the same **or** all
          crystals are white *(1 mark)*
      ii The white solid is pure *(1 mark)*

*Note to parent This question is about pure and
impure substances. You could discuss the
meaning of pure and impure and find examples
around the house. In b) it is essential that the
difference between dissolving and not
dissolving is made, as this is the key to
the process.*

Total 10 marks

3 a) Newton *(1 mark)*
   b) The floor surface, e.g. carpet,
      wood, etc. *(1 mark)*
   c) Shoe has the same mass **or** same
      area is in contact with the floor *(1 mark)*
      *Note to parent If your child has written 'the same
      shoe', they are close. Explain how they can be
      more exact.*

   d) i   Wood *(1 mark)*
      *Note to parent The value for test 2 with wood
      is so much less than test 1 or test 3. Picking
      out incorrect data in a table is an important skill
      your child will need later when they have to
      identify anomalous results.*
      ii Carpet *(1 mark)*
      *Note to parent The largest force was needed
      to move the shoe across the carpet.*
   e) i   Horizontal force – friction *(1 mark)*
      ii Vertical force – weight *(1 mark)*
      *Note to parent The force of friction opposes
      the direction of the pull. The weight is the
      gravitational force of attraction of the shoe
      by the Earth.*

Total 7 marks

4 a) i   The dough rises or expands *(1 mark)*
      ii This makes the loaf lighter *(1 mark)*
   b) i   It is baked in an oven *(1 mark)*
      ii The bread takes on a definite shape, **or**
          changes colour, **or** a hard crust forms.
          (1 mark)
Total 4 marks

5 a) An adult tooth will fill the gap *(1 mark)*
   b) incisor ⟍ ⟋ tearing food
      canine ⟋ ⟍ cutting food
      molar ——— chewing food *(2 marks)*
      All 3 correct – 2 marks
      1 or 2 correct – 1 mark
   c) chocolates *(1 mark)*
      sweets *(1 mark)*
      *Note to parent Allow 1 mark for each correct
      answer but deduct 1 mark for each wrong answer
      (but total not less than zero)*
Total 5 marks

6 a) The Sun makes a shadow
      on a scale *(2 marks)*
      Light from the Sun – 1 mark
      Makes a shadow on a scale – 1 mark
      *Note to parent The word 'shadow' is important.
      If the Sun is out, you could show this with a stick
      in the ground. If the Sun is not out, a lamp could
      be used.*
   b) 2pm **or** 14:00 *(1 mark)*
   c) due south *(1 mark)*
      high in the sky *(1 mark)*
Total 5 marks

Set B Test Paper 2

1 a) copper saucepan, steel knife,
      kitchen foil   *(2 marks)*
      All 3 correct – 2 marks
      1 or 2 correct – 1 mark
      Note to parent *You might sit down with these objects from the kitchen and discuss what properties make each material a metal.*
   b) Glass bowl   *(1 mark)*
   c) Good conductor of heat   *(1 mark)*
   d) Steel knife   *(1 mark)*
   e) candle, plastic spoon, knife   *(2 marks)*
      Candle anywhere before plastic spoon – 1 mark. Plastic spoon anywhere before knife – 1 mark
                                    Total 7 marks

2 a) H drawn on diagram, centre
      of chest   *(1 mark)*
   b) ribs   *(1 mark)*
   c) arteries   *(1 mark)*
   d) veins   *(1 mark)*
      Note to parent *Children need help to remember information. A useful way of remembering this fact is that **ar**teries start with the letter **a**, which matches the letter **a** in **a**way.*
   e) To pump blood   *(1 mark)*
      around the body   *(1 mark)*
                                    Total 6 marks

3 a) Thermometer   *(1 mark)*
   b) 94°C   *(1 mark)*
   c) 65°C   *(1 mark)*
   d) Stir the water   *(1 mark)*
   e) Start at the same temperature   *(1 mark)*
      Temperature falls more slowly   *(1 mark)*
   f) Volume of water   *(1 mark)*
      Starting temperature of the water   *(1 mark)*
                                    Total 8 marks

4 a) **B** turning fast   *(1 mark)*
      C turning slowly   *(1 mark)*
      D not turning   *(1 mark)*
   b) There is not a complete circuit   *(1 mark)*
                                    Total 4 marks

5 a) To remove dirt/germs/microbes
      from their hands   *(1 mark)*
   b) His bread will rise very slowly   *(1 mark)*
      Note to parent *Children often think that yeast only lives in warm temperatures. The idea that microbes are still alive but their rate of reproduction is much slower is a difficult concept.*

   c) The yeast feeds on the sugar   *(1 mark)*
   d) The bread will be flat
      or it will not rise   *(1 mark)*
   e) cheese   *(1 mark)*
      yoghurt   *(1 mark)*
                                    Total 6 marks

6 a) Line from the Sun to the puddle   *(1 mark)*
      Line from the puddle to Rachael   *(1 mark)*

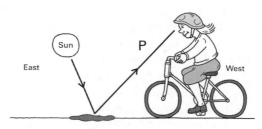

   Deduct 1 mark if lines are not drawn with a ruler and 1 mark if no arrows are shown or if they are in the wrong direction.

   b) Curve drawn as shown on
      the diagram   *(1 mark)*
      Top of the curve marked as
      midday   *(1 mark)*

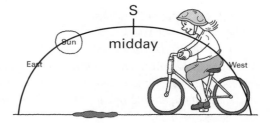

                                    Total 4 marks

7 a) lit torch bulb **and** Sun   *(1 mark)*
      Both required.
   b) It sounds quieter   *(1 mark)*
   c) Accept suitable material, e.g. wood,
      glass, brick   *(1 mark)*
   d) Steven   *(1 mark)*
      Gravitational attraction of the Earth
      (Accept gravity)   *(1 mark)*
                                    Total 5 marks

Set C Test Paper 1

1 a) B *(1 mark)*
   b) The shape of the net *(1 mark)*
      The direction of the ball *(1 mark)*
   c) The ball travels further *(1 mark)*
   d) Gravitational attraction by the Earth *(1 mark)*
      Note to parent *The force is gravitational attraction by the Earth. The word 'gravity' is often used, but 'gravitational attraction' is better.*
      Total 5 marks

2 a) No; Yes *(1 mark)*
      Both must be correct for 1 mark.
   b) The mixture fizzes *(1 mark)*
   c) i Mass would decrease *(1 mark)*
         A gas has been lost from the beaker *(1 mark)*
      ii No change in mass *(1 mark)*
          Nothing is lost from the beaker *(1 mark)*
   d) To keep water from the air out of the tin, to stop the liver salts reacting *(1 mark)*
      Note to parent *This question is emphasising the difference between dissolving and reacting.*
      Total 7 marks

3 a) i skull
      ii ribs
      iii spine *(2 marks)*
      All 3 correct – 2 marks
      2 correct – 1 mark
      1 correct – 0 marks
      Note to parent *Children will not need to learn lots of bones in the skeleton for Key Stage 2. These three are the most likely bones to appear in assessments.*
   b) To support our body *(1 mark)*
      To help us move *(1 mark)*
   c) "My bones can bend in the middle so I can move" is false; the others are true. *(3 marks)*
      All 4 correct – 3 marks
      3 correct – 2 marks
      2 correct – 1 mark
   d) Muscles work harder during exercise *(1 mark)*
      Total 8 marks

4 a) Arrow from chin to mirror *(1 mark)*
      Arrow from mirror to eye *(1 mark)*
      Note to parent *It is not unusual for children to draw the arrows from the eye. It is important to stress that light goes from an object to the eye.*
   b) reflection *(1 mark)*

   c)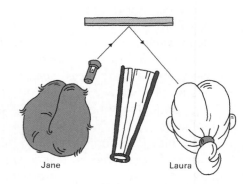

   Straight line from torch to mirror *(1 mark)*
   Light reflected from mirror to Laura *(1 mark)*
   Deduct 1 mark if lines are not drawn with a ruler and 1 mark if arrows are not shown
   d) The piece of paper does not reflect the light ray *(1 mark)*
      Total 6 marks

5 a)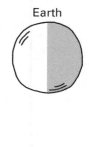
      (1 mark)
   b) Rotate or turn the football *(1 mark)*
   c) Any object much smaller than a football *(1 mark)*
   d)

      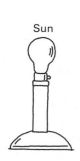

      (1 mark)
      Total 4 marks

6 a) animals   *(1 mark)*
   wind   *(1 mark)*
   b) Seeds start to grow into plants   *(1 mark)*
   c) moisture   *(1 mark)*
      warmth   *(1 mark)*
   Note to parent *A common misconception is that light is needed for germination. Try explaining that seeds are usually under the surface of the soil where light cannot reach.*
   d) Pollination   *(1 mark)*
   Total 6 marks

7 condenses   *(1 mark)*
   evaporates   *(1 mark)*
   vapour   *(1 mark)*
   clouds   *(1 mark)*
   Note to parent *It is important that your child understands this cycle. Sit down and follow the sequence.*
   Total 4 marks

Set C Test Paper 2

1 a) Pond – fish **or** water snail
      (allow heron)   *(1 mark)*
      Field – stoat **or** rabbit (allow heron) *(1 mark)*
   b) Living – any one from: Lee, rabbit, water plants, water snail, fish, heron, grass, stoat
      Non-living – stone
      Both required   *(1 mark)*
   Note to parent *Children often forget that plants are living things.*
   c) Any two from: move, respire (allow breathe), sense, grow, get rid of waste, feed, reproduce   *(2 marks)*
   d) water plants – water snails – fish   *(1 mark)*
      All required for 1 mark
   e) Producer – any one from: grass, water plants   *(1 mark)*
      Prey – any one from: water snail, fish, rabbit   *(1 mark)*
      Predator – any one from: heron, stoat   *(1 mark)*
   Total 9 marks

2 a) A football   *(1 mark)*
   b) 1 False
      2 True
      3 True   *(2 marks)*
      3 correct – 2 marks
      1 or 2 correct – 1 mark
   c)

      (1 mark)

   d)

   (1 mark)
   Total 5 marks

3 a) Ice is less dense than water   *(1 mark)*
   b) i Thermometer   *(1 mark)*
      ii 0°C   *(1 mark)*
   c) i Reversible *(No mark for 'reversible' alone)*. Can be reversed by putting water into a freezer   *(1 mark)*
      ii Melting   *(1 mark)*
      iii Water vapour in the atmosphere *(1 mark)*
          condenses on the cold glass   *(1 mark)*
   d) The temperature is lower   *(1 mark)*
   Note to parent *Remind your child that salt is put onto frozen roads in winter. This melts the ice.*
   Total 8 marks

4 a) It was warmer in the greenhouse   *(1 mark)*
      Different cress seeds were used to grow the plants   *(1 mark)*
   b) Can't tell   *(1 mark)*
      True   *(1 mark)*
      Can't tell   *(1 mark)*
      False   *(1 mark)*
   Note to parent *Children find this type of question difficult. They need to keep in mind only the conditions the experiment can show. Their understanding that plants in greenhouses grow better will distract them from the question of practical skills.*
   c) roots   *(1 mark)*
   Total 7 marks

5   a) dissolve   *(1 mark)*
    b) To see if he gets the same or
       similar results   *(1 mark)*
       Note to parent *The answer to b) is not that*
       repeating the results ensures a fair test.
    c) Second experiment with icing
       sugar   *(1 mark)*
    d) As the grains get smaller, the time for
       dissolving is shorter
       or as the grains get larger, the time for
       dissolving increases   *(2 marks)*
       Note to parent *It is important that a comparison*
       is made here for 2 marks. This is sometimes
       called an ... er -... er statement. As the grains get
       *small**er**, the time for dissolving is short**er**. This is*
       an important idea your child must develop in KS2.
    e) Amount of stirring   *(1 mark)*
    f) Heat or use hot water   *(1 mark)*
                                    Total 7 marks

6   a) The elastic band could break   *(1 mark)*
    b) 4 (cm)   *(1 mark)*
    c) 10 (cm)   *(1 mark)*
    d) As the number of masses increases, the
       length of the elastic band increases
                                                   (1 mark)
                                    Total 4 marks